Usborne Work[s]

Grammar
and
Punctuation

This book belongs to

....

There's a list of useful grammar and
punctuation words on page 27, and notes
for grown-ups at the back of the book.

Here are some of the animals you'll meet in this book. They are learning about grammar and punctuation.

Wolfy

an
egg

Hop

an
apple

Ping

a
cake

Gloria

a
banana

Pin

an
ice cream

Zeb

a
carrot

Help the animals by using a pen or pencil to draw and write on each page.

Usborne Workbooks
Grammar
and
Punctuation

Illustrated by Elisa Paganelli

Written by Hannah Watson
Designed by Maddison Warnes

strawberry

an
orange

cherry

Bruce

There are extra pages
at the back of the book
for more grammar and
punctuation practice.

Kat

Pat

Edited by Kristie Pickersgill
Series Editor: Felicity Brooks

'a' or 'an'?

The animals are thinking about the starting sounds of words.
Can you help them sort their words into boxes to show if they
start with a vowel or a consonant sound? Draw a line between
each word and the box it belongs to.

Vowel sounds are normally made by the letters a, e, i, o and u.
The other letters of the alphabet usually make a consonant sound.

apricot

feather

Be careful
with me.

insect

leaf

stone

egg

Hmmmm,
let me
see...

How many
do you
have, Hop?

orange

vowel
sounds

consonant
sounds

Ping and his friends are talking about the things they have found.
Write 'a' or 'an' in the gaps to finish the sentences in their speech bubbles.

When a word begins with a vowel sound, use 'an'. When a word begins with a consonant sound, use 'a'. Using 'a' and 'an' correctly makes a phrase much easier to say.

I found .... rock and .... feather.

I've got .... insect! I'll put him back in his home now.

Did you find .... egg, Bruce?

Yes, and I picked up .... leaf.

Wolfy has written some sentences about the day.
Tick the ones that are correct.

Today, we went on a walk. ☐ Afterwards, I had an ice cream. ☐

It was an sunny morning. ☐ We had such a interesting day. ☐

Word families

A word family is a group of words that are related
to each other by their grammar, meaning and spelling.

The animals are at the beach today and Bruce
needs help to pick some coconuts. Draw a
coconut shape around all the words that
contain the word 'help'.
(Your shapes can
overlap.)

helpful

hope

unhelpful

helper

help

hot

handful

helpless

Help!

help _ _ _ _

We'll
help you!

_ _ help _ _ _

help _ _ _ _

help _ _

Use the words in the 'help' word family on the tree to write
in the spaces and label the scene. Look carefully at how each
word begins or ends to help you decide which one to use.

Hop and Gloria are thinking of word families to describe the beach, but they have chosen some words that don't belong. Draw a line through six words that don't fit in the families.

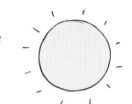

sand
seaside
sandy
sandcastle
seagull

sun
stream
sunshine
sunset
starfish

land
island
landmark
lagoon
lifeguard

Kat, Zeb and Pin are fishing in a rockpool. They can only catch fish that belong to their word family. Draw a line from each word to the correct bucket.

Clauses

A main clause makes complete sense on its own.

A subordinate clause depends on a main clause for its meaning.

Bruce loves cooking.

Bruce loves cooking because he can eat the leftovers.

Today, the animals are having lunch at a café. There are four sentences about them below. Some have just a main clause, and some have a main clause and a subordinate clause. Draw a straight line under all the main clauses.

Wolfy ordered some chocolate cake.

Pin can't eat nuts because she's allergic to them.

Gloria loves pineapple.

Zeb ordered two pizzas so everyone could share them.

Now draw a wiggly line under the subordinate clauses and a star next to sentences that contain both a main and a subordinate clause.

In the kitchen, Hop has torn up Bruce's instructions by mistake.
Draw a line from each main clause on the left to the correct
subordinate clause on the right so that the instructions make sense.

1. Always wash your hands

if you don't like them.

2. Keep an eye on the timer

so the food doesn't burn.

3. You can leave out the nuts

before you start to cook.

Write an instruction that could go in a recipe. Start with a main clause,
then give more information by adding a subordinate clause.

....

....

....

Conjunctions

Conjunctions are used to link words and clauses.
They can help describe the time, place or cause of something.

The animals are chatting about their camping trip. Cross out the wrong conjunction so each sentence makes sense.

Put on your coat
while / so you
don't get cold.

Let's light the fire,
so / because
it's cold.

We need to finish
after / before
it gets too dark!

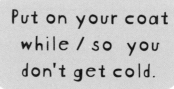

When / While
we're finished,
let's relax.

While / After I'm
finding wood, can
you get water?

Yes, next / after I
have found the rope.

Can you underline one conjunction in each of these sentences?

Kat likes marshmallows and cocoa.

Wolfy would help but he has hurt his paw.

Gloria is scared because she doesn't like the dark.

Ping gave Gloria a torch so she could see.

Can you circle all of the conjunctions in the green box below?

| so | | for | | because | | and |
| | people | | but | | blue | |

Now, write your own sentence about camping using one of the conjunctions.

....

....

....

Now, pick a different conjunction and write another sentence.

....

....

....

Adverbs

Adverbs such as 'quickly' or 'easily' describe an action. Adverbs such as 'then', 'here' or 'therefore' tell you when, where or why an action happened.

Fill in the gaps in the sentences below using the adverbs at the top of the card.

there   then   everywhere   soon

We crossed a river and _____ we ate our picnic.

The sun came out and _____ it was really hot.

We looked _____ for Kat.

She was waiting _____ for us on the other side of the river.

Help Kat jump across the river. Trace the dotted line, then continue it to show where she can land. She needs to land on all the rocks with adverbs on them, but none of the others.

Prepositions

Prepositions such as 'behind' or 'after' describe where something is in relation to something else, or when something happened.

Ping is collecting stones that have prepositions on them. Kat is collecting the others. Draw lines from each stone to the correct bucket.

Hmmmm...

Ping's prepositions

during   sadly

fun   in   on

under   little

Kat's other words

Choose the correct preposition from the green box to finish the sentences below. Remember to use a capital letter if the word comes at the start of a sentence.

before   under   after

because of   in

I hid _ _ _ _ _ _ the blanket _ _ _ _ _ _ _ _ _ the storm.

_ _ _ _ _ _ I tried coconut, I thought I didn't like it.

_ _ _ _ _ _ we had eaten our lunch, we paddled _ _ the sea.

Direct speech

Direct speech is when you write the exact words someone has said. You put inverted commas (" ") around the words to show that it is speech.

The animals are dressed up for a parade in the park. There are a few sentences about them below. Put a dot next to those that contain direct speech.

Zeb asked if he looked funny.

Pin's costume was yellow with black spots.

"I love dressing up," said Kat.

"Do you like my hat?" asked Wolfy.

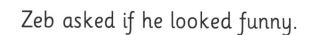

Inverted commas are also called speech marks.

Now draw a ring around all the inverted commas (" ") you can find. Then, underline the part of the sentence that is direct speech.

Inverted commas look a little like clothes pegs. Can you peg the clothes to the line by drawing pairs of inverted commas? (The first pair has been done for you.)

I can't reach!

Ping is writing a story. Draw a star next to the sentences where he has used inverted commas correctly.

The Park Parade

"one day, the animals were trying on costumes for the parade".

"oh dear! Can you help me?" shouted Gloria.

"what's the matter?" asked Wolfy.

"I've got" stuck! sighed Gloria.

Add the missing inverted commas to these sentences.

What time is the parade? asked Zeb.

Three o'clock, Ping replied.

Wolfy added, Don't be late!

Do you like my costume for the parade?

The present perfect

The present perfect tense is formed with the verb 'to have' and the past participle of a verb.

You can use the present perfect tense to talk about things in the past which have continued up to the present.

the verb 'to have'

the past participle of the verb 'to play'

I <u>have played</u> the drums since I was five.

The animals are talking about their lives in the animal park. Rewrite their verbs in the present perfect tense by writing 'I have' instead of 'I'. Use the example to help you.

Because the animals are describing things that they continue to do, they need to use the present perfect tense.

I lived in the park from the age of three.

I have lived in the park from the age of three.

I worked in the café for five months.

I..in the café for five months.

I helped at the parade every year.

I..at the parade every year.

You can also use the present perfect to talk about things that happened in the past that have an effect on the present.

Pin and Hop are playing a memory game. Pin memorizes the things on the tray, then closes her eyes while Hop moves some or takes some away.

I **have played** this game with Pin and Hop. Do you want a turn?

Pin **has closed** her eyes!

I **have changed** something.

Because the actions in the past affect the present, Hop **has used** the present perfect tense.

Have they **finished** yet?

Pin has written a sentence about one thing that Hop has changed while her eyes were closed. Write another, using the word list on the right to help you.

squawk!

Hop has moved the pen. ....

....

Can you use the present perfect to describe another thing that has changed? Write your sentence below.

....

....

moved
taken
changed
hidden

More present perfect

When something happens in a period of time that hasn't finished yet, such as a day, a week, a month or a year, you use the present perfect.

You can also use the present perfect tense to talk about things you have done in your life.

The busy animals always keep a note of what they have done in their diaries. Look at these diary pages for clues to help you finish the sentences. (The first one has been done for you.)

I _have_ _visited_ Italy three times on holiday.

Zeb's week

Monday – Went swimming
Tuesday
Wednesday – Swimming lesson
Thursday
Friday
Saturday – Swim with friends

Zeb has been swimming three times

this week.

Wolfy's month

Week 1 – Visited Grandma
Week 2
Week 3 – Visited Grandma
Week 4

Wolfy

Grandma twice this month.

Kat and Ping's year

January – Took train to France

August – Took train to beach

October – Took train to zoo

Kat and Ping

the train three times this year.

Present perfect practice

Bruce is writing about his friend Zeb, but he has made some mistakes. Draw a line under four mistakes.

I has been best friends with Zeb since I was little.

We have know each other for three years.

Zeb has plays at my house every week since we meet.

Gloria is sending out party invitations. See if you can rewrite the invitation, using the present perfect tense for the sentence that has a line under it.

Please come to my party.

I made a cake and Mum

hired a bouncy castle.

It will be lots of fun!
Gloria x

Please come to my party.

I ....

.... a cake and Mum ....

.... a bouncy castle.

It will be lots of fun!

Gloria X

Read Pin's diary entry about her week. Draw a line under each place she has used the present perfect tense.

Dear Diary,

I am having a great week. I have visited the café twice.

I have been to the art gallery and my dad has promised

to take me swimming. I hope next week is as much fun!

20

Paragraphs

A paragraph is a group of sentences on a similar topic.

Ping and Kat have each written a paragraph but the sentences are muddled up. Draw lines to link three sentences that belong in the same paragraph so each one makes sense.

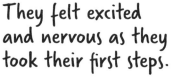

I've done the first link!

The astronauts climbed down out of their landing module.	The princess paused for a moment in front of the dragon's lair.
Suddenly, she heard a loud roar from deep within the cave.	Their huge boots sank deep into the dust on the planet's surface.
Would she be able to tame the terrifying dragon?	They felt excited and nervous as they took their first steps.

The Princess and the Dragon by Kat

Space Adventure by Ping

Woah!

Decide whether the sentences belong in Kat's story or Ping's story, then draw a line from the last sentence of each paragraph to the correct book.

Paragraphs and headings

You often need to begin a new paragraph when you are talking about a new idea or character, or a different time or place.

Gloria is writing a report about swimming, but she has forgotten to use paragraphs. Divide the report into three paragraphs by putting a stroke (/) in two places where a new paragraph should begin.

Ping is a champion swimmer. He has been swimming since he was little and he has won ten medals. You can swim in the sea, or at a swimming pool. Swimming in the sea is fun but can be dangerous! You must make sure there is a lifeguard present. In the past, you had to hold your breath to swim underwater. It was hard to stay under the water for long without equipment. With scuba tanks, it's much easier to explore coral reefs than it was long ago.

Gloria is thinking up a heading for her swimming report.
Put a tick next to the one you think is best.

Sports Review   All About Swimming   At the Beach

Which sub-heading is most suitable for each paragraph in Gloria's report?
Write a), b) or c) next to each paragraph you have marked above.

a) Swimming in the sea   b) A swimming star   c) Swimming long ago

Writing practice

Help Hop correct her diary by writing out each sentence correctly. Look back through the book for clues to help you.

I think I've made a few mistakes. Can you help me?

Yesterday, I went to an party for Zeb.

Pin said to me, "I has forgotten a gift!

Luckily, "Bruce helped us buy a great present".

It was a fun day and I have a lovely time.

Hop is thinking of a heading for her diary entry to sum up her day. Draw a ring around the best heading to describe what she did.

Zeb's Birthday Party

Gift Ideas

A Shopping Trip

Choose words from the box to fill in the gaps in Wolfy's story.

| soon | had | ship | before |
| beside | because of | so | in |

It was midnight, _ _ the sailors were

asleep _ _ their bunks. Suddenly, the

ship rocked violently. The sailors were

terrified _ _ _ _ _ _ _ _ _ the stories

they _ _ _ heard about sea monsters.

They thought it was something scary.

However, they _ _ _ _ learned it was just

a submarine!

Fill in the missing words for me, please.

Kat and Pin are praising Wolfy's story.
Draw a ring around all the words in the same word family.

Superb!   Great!

Super!

Fantastic!   Supreme!

Grammar and punctuation quiz

Find out how much you can remember about grammar and punctuation by doing this quiz. Answers on page 26.

1. Write 'a' or 'an' in each gap to complete the sentences.

a) I ate .... orange.

b) She found .... leaf.

c) What .... amazing insect.

2. Put a tick in the boxes next to the words in the same word family.

a) sunshine ☐   d) sunrise ☐

b) sand ☐   e) seagull ☐

c) sundial ☐   f) sunset ☐

3. Put a tick in the box next to all the sentences that contain a main clause and a subordinate clause.

a) Wolfy loves strawberry ice cream. ☐

b) Kat prefers vanilla because it's tasty. ☐

c) Zeb can't choose, so he has a scoop of both. ☐

d) Ping doesn't like ice cream. ☐

Mmmmm, strawberry ice cream!

4. Choose the correct conjunction from this box to complete each of these sentences.

but   and   because

a) Hop likes singing .... dancing.

b) Pin would have played outside, ... it was raining.

c) Gloria made a cake .... it was Wolfy's birthday.

5. Which of the underlined words are adverbs, and which are prepositions? Write 'A' in the box for an adverb, and 'P' for a preposition.

a) We drank hot chocolate; <u>next</u>, we sang a campfire song. ☐

b) I hid <u>under</u> the blanket because of the storm. ☐

c) We thought it would rain; <u>however</u>, it was sunny. ☐

6. These sentences contain direct speech. Tick two boxes for each sentence to show where inverted commas should go.

i) Can you come to my party? asked Gloria.

a) ☐   b) ☐   c) ☐   d) ☐

ii) Pat replied with a big smile, I would love to!

a) ☐   b) ☐   c) ☐   d) ☐

7. Rewrite this sentence in the present perfect tense.

Zeb helped at the park parade every year.

....

....

8. Gloria, Zeb and Kat have each written a book review about one of the books below. Read the headings and sub-headings, then draw a line to match the right headings to the right book title.

a) Oceans and Shipwrecks   b) Castles and Kingdoms   c) Out of This World
      All at Sea   A Royal Treat   A Space Adventure

1.

2.

3.

Quiz answers

1. a) 'an' b) 'a' c) 'an'   2. a), c), d), f)   3. b), c)

4. a) and b) but c) because   5. a) A b) P c) A   6. i) a), c)

                                                     ii) c), d)

7. Zeb has helped at the park parade every year.

8. a) 1.   b) 3.   c) 2.

Score 1 point for each correct answer and write your score in this box:

23

Grammar and punctuation words

adverb – a word such as 'then', 'here' or 'therefore' that tells you when, where or why an action happened. (Other types of adverbs, for example 'quickly' and 'bravely', describe an action.)

conjunction – a word or phrase that links two words or clauses together, for example 'and', 'for' or 'so'.

consonant sound – a sound usually made by the letters in the alphabet that are not vowels. You use 'a' rather than 'an' before a consonant sound, for example 'a kite' not 'an kite'.

direct speech – when you write the exact words someone has said.

inverted commas – punctuation marks (" ") that indicate direct speech. They are also called speech marks or quotation marks.

main clause – part of a sentence that makes complete sense on its own.

preposition – a word that describes where something is in relation to something else, or when something happened, for example 'before' or 'under'.

subordinate clause – part of a sentence that depends on a main clause for its meaning. A subordinate clause is normally introduced by a conjunction.

vowel sound – a sound usually made by the letters a, e, i, o, u and sometimes y. You use 'an' rather than 'a' before a vowel sound, for example 'an apple', not 'a apple'.

word family – a group of words that are related to each other by their grammar, meaning and spelling, for example 'teach, teacher and teaching'.

28

You can use these pages for writing practice.

You could use this page to write about what you've done today.

Can you underline the conjunctions you have used?

The egg is
in the nest.

Can you use
prepositions to
describe the things
on this page?

I love swimming.
I have been swimming
every week for
3 years.

You could write about
your favourite thing
to do on this page.

Did you use the
present perfect in
your writing?

Notes for grown-ups

'a' or 'an'? (pages 4-5)

This introduces children to the link between vowel and consonant sounds and the use of the indefinite articles 'a' and 'an'. Children could be encouraged to see that it is the consonant and vowel sound that is important, rather than the first letter of a word. This is why we write 'a unicorn', and 'an honest mistake'.

Word families (pages 6-7)

These pages encourage children to recognize words that are connected by spelling, grammar or meaning, and make logical links as they read. Children could think up their own word families.

Clauses (pages 8-9)

This helps explain the role of clauses in a sentence. Children may see that a subordinate clause relies on a main clause for its meaning, and adds information. They may realize that a subordinate clause can come first in a sentence, followed by a comma and then the main clause.

Conjunctions (pages 10-11)

This allows children to practise locating conjunctions in a sentence, and out of context, and also to choose the right conjunction to complete the meaning of a sentence. They could be encouraged to use conjunctions to make their own writing more complex.

Adverbs/Prepositions (pages 12-13)

These pages show the role of adverbs as conjunctions and also prepositions in linking parts of a sentence. Adverbs such as 'then', 'here' or 'therefore' tell you when, where or why an action happened. Adverbs such as 'quickly' or 'easily' describe an action.

Direct speech (pages 14-15)

These pages introduce direct speech as the recording of someone's words, and the use of inverted commas to punctuate it. Children could practise turning reported speech into direct speech.

The present perfect (pages 16-17)

This shows how to form the present perfect tense. Children can use the present perfect tense in the context of things in the past that have continued into the present, or events in the past that affect the present.

More present perfect/Present perfect practice (pages 18-19)

These pages show how the present perfect can be used to describe something happening in a period of time that hasn't yet finished. Summary activities consolidate children's understanding of how this tense is used.

Paragraphs/Paragraphs and headings (pages 20-21)

This allows children to see how paragraphs, headings and sub-headings can be used to group related material. You could explain that headings and sub-headings can be used to aid presentation and make writing more formal, such as in reports and book reviews.

Writing practice (pages 22-23)

The diary activity allows children to recap indefinite articles (4-5), the present perfect tense (16-19), direct speech (14-15) and headings (21). The story activity covers conjunctions (10-11), prepositions (13), adverbs as conjunctions (12), the present perfect tense (16-19) and word families (6-7).